A special thanks
to everyone
who has helped make
Know Yourself
what it is today.

Dear Reader

Knowing yourself is truly the beginning of all wisdom. We give young learners the building blocks they need to start their unique journey of self-discovery: an understanding of human anatomy — literally how we are put together. Knowledge of one's own human body is an empowering context on which anyone can build.

Learning about the body and mind at a young age sets the foundation for honoring one's physical form, develops self-esteem and self-confidence, and begins the discovery of who we are meant to be in this world.

Now that's real power.

The Know Yourself Team

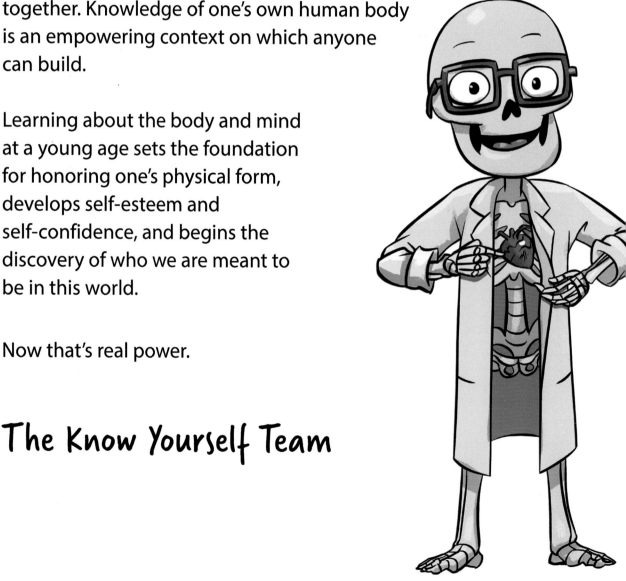

Quick-Start Guide
Hello Know Yourselfers!

Follow these steps to start a new journey and explore the nervous system. Have fun on this quest and remember - keep the information flowing!

1

Grab your ulu and canoe - we're going to Guadalcanal!

Find the Solomon Islands on your atlas, or find an online map of the world.

2

Read Time Skaters Adventure 11.

Pinky, Naz and Shorty deal with an overloaded Hank! Will they be able to find the next clue despite the dangers of a World War?

3

Get equipped!

Search for your supplies listed on the home inventory page. Don't be nervous, you'll be able to think your way through it!

Table of Contents

Hello Adventurer!

Welcome to Adventure 11 - The Nervous System.

In this workbook, you will learn about Guadalcanal, Solomon Islands and your body's Nervous System. There will be information to read, activities to complete, and quizzes to take when you are ready to challenge yourself! Take your time along the way - spend as much or as little time as you like on each activity.

Good luck, and have fun!

Destination: Guadalcanal, Solomon Islands!

THE TIME TRAVEL CLOCK READS

1859

Let's get moving!

LEARN ABOUT
The Nervous System

Taking everything you sense and sending that information where it needs to go!

VISIT
Guadalcanal in 1942

Just like the Solomon Islanders, the Time Skaters find themselves in the middle of war.

MEET
The Navajo Code Talkers

With a complex code made from an unwritten language, these soldiers braved battles to keep information flowing securely.

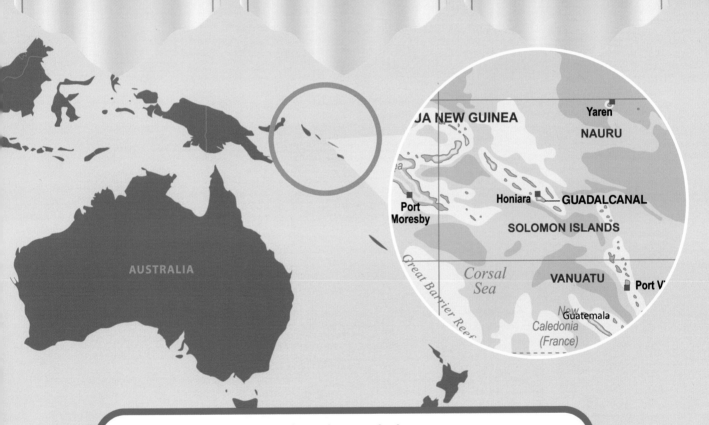

JA NEW GUINEA

Yaren

NAURU

Port Moresby

Honiara — GUADALCANAL

SOLOMON ISLANDS

AUSTRALIA

Corsal Sea

Great Barrier Reef

VANUATU

Port V

New Caledonia (France)

Guatemala

Yá'át'ééh*

That means "Welcome" in Navajo, the language of the Native American tribe, the Navajo, or the Diné.

*Say it like this: "ya-ah-TEH"

The strongest syllable is shown in CAPITALS.

Enter this portal for....

Time Skaters Adventure 11
Keep Calm and Neuron!

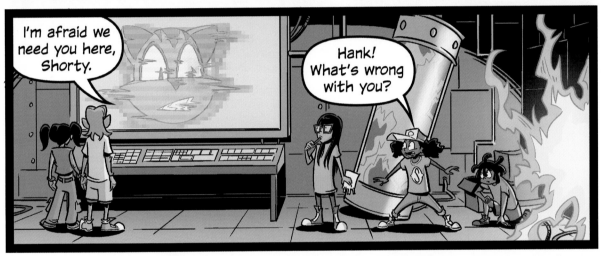

Every part of your body is in some way controlled by the **Nervous System**: the brain, spinal cord, and a huge network of nerves.

The nervous system can be divided into: 1) the **central nervous system**, and 2) the **peripheral nervous system**. Each has its own unique parts.

Commander in Chief: Your Brain. The brain and spinal cord make up your **central nervous system**.

The adult **brain** is about 3 pounds of wrinkly, gray, sponge-like organ floating inside the skull.

This amazing and complex structure is constantly hard at work transmitting signals throughout the body.

Your brain controls how you think and what you think, feel, dream, and do. It's what makes you, you!

Brain

Spinal Chord

Vertebrae

Straight from The Top: Your Spinal Cord. Messages from your brain travel via your spinal cord, a delicate, tube-like structure made of nervous tissue. It extends from the brain stem all the way down to the base of your spinal column.

Protected by your **vertebrae,** * the spinal cord allows your brain to communicate with the rest of your body by bringing in, integrating, and sending out information.

*Say it like this: VER-tuh-bray

Brain Flash: Vertebrae (one is called a vertebra) are special bones that protect your spinal cord. Stacked on top of each other, they are also able to move – kind of like a chain of beads.

SYNAPSE

SYNAPSE

SYNAPSE

While your brain is literally head commander, it requires a lot of help to keep you moving and functioning.

Enter millions of neurons – microscopic cells that branch and reach toward each other to send signals from the brain to the rest of your body. However, at the junction where they connect, the **synapse,** they don't actually touch.

Messages jump from from one neuron to the next, rapid-fire, like lightning. From thought to action, a brain signal travels between 70-120 miles per second. That's *fast!*

Neurons

Synapses

Think of your neurons like soldiers or members of a team. The strength of your nervous system's operation is in the connections: your neurons' ability to communicate and work together.

11

That was too close!

We should probably stay out of sight from now on.

It's working beyond our wildest dreams!

Our best cryptographers can't begin to crack it!

Best of all, they can translate the code with near-perfect accuracy in mere seconds!

You're very trusting, Mr. Johnston...

Actually, now it's Staff Sergeant Johnston.

I just don't understand.

How can something this easy by working so well?

Sir, these men have already outperformed their peers in basic training. The other men find them intelligent and they are good at their jobs.

The question remains, Johnston, how do you know this is going to work?

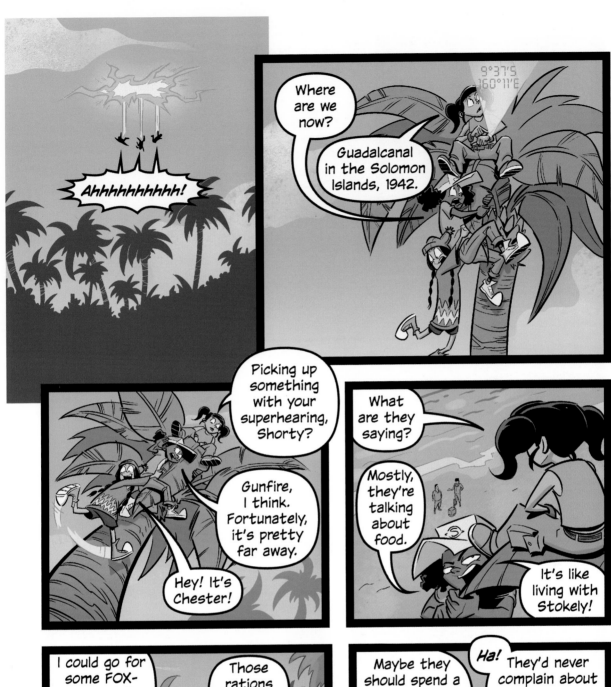

Ahhhhhhhhh!

Where are we now?

Guadalcanal in the Solomon Islands, 1942.

9°37'S 160°11'E

Picking up something with your superhearing, Shorty?

Gunfire, I think. Fortunately, it's pretty far away.

Hey! It's Chester!

What are they saying?

Mostly, they're talking about food.

It's like living with Stokely!

I could go for some FOX-ONION-OWL-DEER* about now!

Those rations are good, huh?

I can't believe the other men hate them so much.

*A lot of Navajo code involved using words in place of letters. Fox: F + Onion: O + Owl: O + Deer: D = FOOD.

Maybe they should spend a week protecting sheep on a reservation in the rain!

Ha! They'd never complain about rations – or anything else – again!

You mean the Long Walk?

In 1863, the American military forced the Navajo into camps.

And in 1930, the government decided we kept too many animals. Men came to thin our herds..

Many of us are still trying to recover.

Still, even before Japan attacked Pearl Harbor, the Navajo leadership released a statement saying we were ready to fight to defend the United States.

Many of us were eager to volunteer to protect our homeland.

After all, our ancestors lived there long before anyone else.

20

All your nerves outside of the brain and spinal cord belong to the **peripheral nervous system (PNS)**.

Like tiny wires, your nerves transmit communication signals throughout the body. With so much information to handle, the peripheral nervous system needs to be organized!

Central Nervous System (CNS)

Peripheral Nervous System (PNS)

Branching out from the spinal cord, nerves **innervate*** every part of your body.

Sensory (Afferent) Division

Collects information from our senses (touch, taste, smell, feel, sight) and sends it toward the brain. **A**fferent=**A**wareness

Motor (Efferent) Division

Motor = movement! Sends signals from the CNS to muscles and glands.

Sympathetic Nervous System (SNS)

The SNS helps us respond to stress quickly: "fight or flight" mode!

Autonomic* Nervous System

Auto = self-run. Affects the body's involuntary, non-sensory thinking activities: breath, digestion, heart rate.

Somatic* Nervous System

Soma = body. Affects voluntary activities such as talking, walking. Also sends the brain sensory info to process. Messages skeletal muscles to get your body moving!

Parasympathetic Nervous System (PSNS)

The PSNS helps us do what we need to do the rest of the time: rest, digest

*Say it like this: IN-ner-vate, ah-tow-NOM-ik, so-MAT-ik

24

HOORAY FOR LOBE

Probably the most recognizable part of your brain is the **cerebrum.***

We Can Do It!

Your cerebrum has four lobes: **frontal, parietal, temporal** and **occipital.** Each lobe has several functions, but primarily:

Occipital = vision
Temporal = memory and sound
Parietal = sensory (touch, taste)
Frontal = thinking

Of these four lobes, it's the frontal lobe that's in charge of personality, problem solving, and decision making. It's the lobe that says, "You can do it!"

This part of your brain also produces and understands speech. It plans, analyzes, and integrates sensory information.

Your brain is the boss, but that boss ALSO has a boss: your frontal lobe!

*Say it like this: Suh-REE-brum

BRAIN FLASH: Have you noticed it's hard to think when you're tired or hungry? When under stress or low on fuel, the brain feeds the back lobes first to keep you functioning and alive. Your brain's #1 job is survival!

Unhhh...

He'll be all right.

My head...

Thanks for looking after my buddy, girls.

I've got to get him to a medic.

I can take you girls to our camp.

Don't worry about us. We'll find our way home safely.

Well, thank you again, girls!

Can't leave you alone in a firefight for even a minute...

Wait, Chester!

Before you passed out, you said something about the three of us and...a bone hand?

Chester, do you know what she is talking about?

Yes... at least I think I do.

TRADING POST

It happened one night while I was working at the trading post in New Mexico, before I enlisted in the Marines.

He was covered from head to toe, so I couldn't see what he looked like.

He told me I'd meet three girls somewhere they didn't belong.

I was supposed to give them a message.

For a long time, I was afraid of him, because when he handed me the mssage, he was made of bone!

But if he put you in my path, he couldn't possibly be bad.

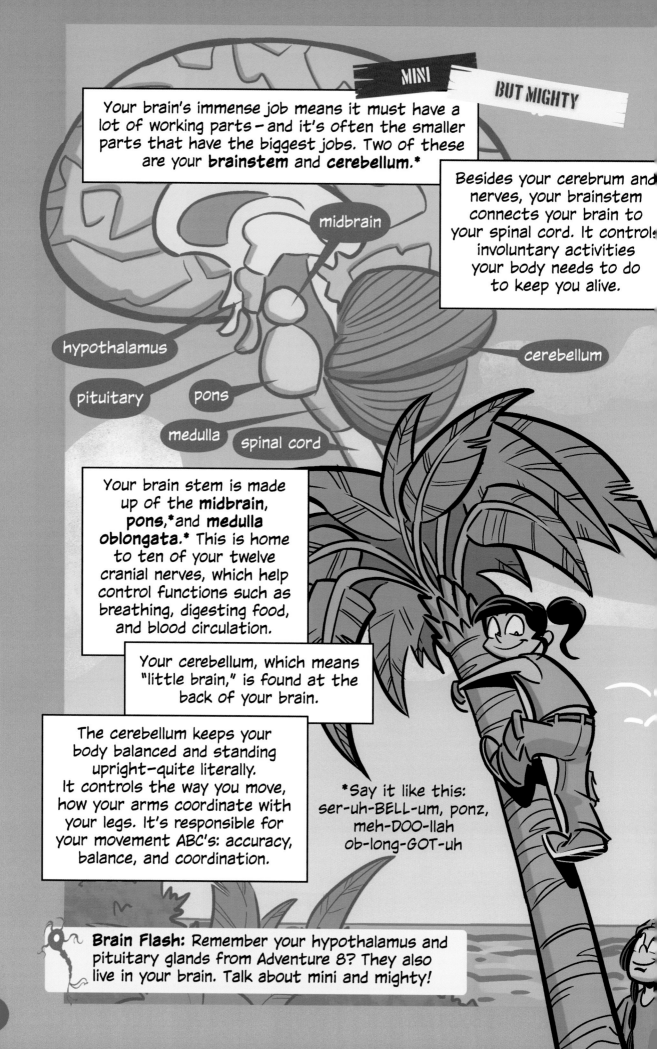

Your brain's immense job means it must have a lot of working parts—and it's often the smaller parts that have the biggest jobs. Two of these are your **brainstem** and **cerebellum.***

Besides your cerebrum and nerves, your brainstem connects your brain to your spinal cord. It controls involuntary activities your body needs to do to keep you alive.

midbrain

hypothalamus

cerebellum

pituitary

pons

medulla

spinal cord

Your brain stem is made up of the **midbrain, pons,***and **medulla oblongata.*** This is home to ten of your twelve cranial nerves, which help control functions such as breathing, digesting food, and blood circulation.

Your cerebellum, which means "little brain," is found at the back of your brain.

The cerebellum keeps your body balanced and standing upright—quite literally. It controls the way you move, how your arms coordinate with your legs. It's responsible for your movement ABC's: accuracy, balance, and coordination.

*Say it like this: ser-uh-BELL-um, ponz, meh-DOO-llah ob-long-GOT-uh

Brain Flash: Remember your hypothalamus and pituitary glands from Adventure 8? They also live in your brain. Talk about mini and mighty!

30

The brain sits cushioned in spinal fluid inside the skull. If your head is struck or shaken, the brain can bang against the skull, which can bruise your brain, damaging blood vessels and nerves. After Chester was blown back by the blast, he had a slight concussion. Do you remember which of these symptoms he had?

Confusion
Difficulty walking
Loss of consciousness
Difficulty speaking
Blurred vision
Saying things that don't make sense
Unresponsiveness/ won't wake up
Headaches

After a concussion, doctors focus on your 12 cranial nerves (CN), which branch off the brainstem. Look at where they are located and what they control:

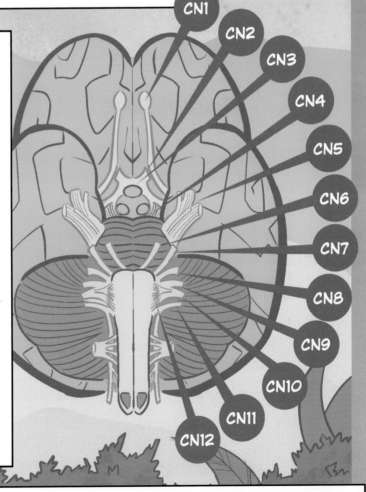

In the front of your brain:
CN1 (Smell)
CN2 (Vision)

In your midbrain:
CN3, CN4 (Eye movement)

In your pons:
CN5 (Muscles and senses of the face, chewing)
CN6 (More eye movement, away from your center)
CN7 (Taste, facial expressions)
CN8 (Hearing and balance)

In your medulla:
CN9 (Taste, throat, humming)
CN10 (Throat, voice, coughing, glands, digestion, heart rate)
CN11 (Rotating your head, shrugging your shoulders, raising your chin)
CN12 (Muscles of your tongue)

Since your cranial nerves live deep in your brain and brainstem, getting hit in the head is sort of like a big earthquake for them. It's important to give your brain time to repair and recover after being hurt, just like you would for any injury.

31

Learning Calendar

Part 1
Know Your History

Dive Into *Know Your History.*

Get to *Know Your Navajo Culture.*

Seek to *Know your Codes* the **Try** *I Put a Spell on You*

Learn about *Know Your Na'atl'lo* and **Play** Navajo String Games with to *I've Got the World on a String*

Find out *Solomon Island Secrets*

Brave wild waters in *Can You Canoe*

Crack *the Code*

Part 2
Know Your Nervous System

Peruse Know Your Science

Galvanize your mind and solve your *Need for Neurons*

Master regions of the *A-MAZE-ing Brain*

Travel to 1942 and *Know Your Maps, then* **Go** *Dome, Sweet Dome*

Make your connections at *Synapse Station*

Do the *Brain Bop*

Part **3**

Know
Your
Appetite

Build up your hunger with *Know Your Appetite*

Prepare *Victory Garden Salad* and *Cottage Cheese and Green Onion Muffins*

Share your dishes with your family. *Discuss Thoughts for Young Chefs* around the table!

Part **4**

Show
What You
Know!

Prove your *Epic Brainpower*

Great job on all your hard work!

Home Inventory Checklist

Ask your parents to help you find these items around the house. These are some of the tools you will need on your adventure. Don't worry if you can't find every single one - you'll be able to use your imagination.

☐ **1 piece of paper**
 - Can You Canoe

☐ **½ cup of wax (unscented)**
 - Can You Canoe

☐ **Microwave safe container**
 - Can You Canoe

☐ **Paintbrush**
 - Can You Canoe

☐ **Microwave**
 - Can You Canoe

☐ **3 colors of playdough** (See "Making Materials" to make your own)
 - Need for Neurons

☐ **Flat, clean space for rolling**
 - Need for Neurons

☐ **Ruler or measuring tape**
 - Need for Neurons
 - Know About Strokes: Bonus Activity

☐ **2 cups all-purpose flour**
 - Making Materials: Bonus Activity

☐ **¾ cup salt**
 - Making Materials: Bonus Activity

☐ **4 teaspoons cream of tartar**
 - Making Materials: Bonus Activity

- [ ] **2 cups room temperature water**
  - Making Materials: Bonus Activity

- [ ] **2 tablespoons vegetable or coconut oil**
  - Making Materials: Bonus Activity

- [ ] **3 colors of food coloring** (Red, Yellow and Green work well)
  - Making Materials: Bonus Activity

- [ ] **1 large pot**
  - Making Materials: Bonus Activity

- [ ] **3 quart sized bags**
  - Making Materials: Bonus Activity

- [ ] **Dominoes or polymer clay**
  - Know About Strokes: Bonus Activity

- [ ] **Rolling pin**
  - Know About Strokes: Bonus Activity

- [ ] **Pencil**
  - Know About Strokes: Bonus Activity
  - A-MAZE-ing Brain)

- [ ] **Metal spatula**
  - Know About Strokes: Bonus Activity

- [ ] **Baking sheet**
  - Know About Strokes: Bonus Activity

- [ ] **Oven**
  - Know About Strokes: Bonus Activity

Don't worry if you can't find every single item – just use your imagination and find substitutions!

✓ Check the items off when you've found them!

Solomon Islands, 1942

World War II Pacific Theater

WWII was a global war that involved over 30 countries but mainly the **Allies*** (the U.S., Great Britain, the Soviet Union, France, and China) and the **Axis*** (Germany, Japan, and Italy).

*Say it like this:
allies - "**AL-eyes**"
axis - "**AX-iss**"

The strongest syllable is always shown in **CAPITALS** and **red**.

Many people left their homes to go many other places around the world. In the comic, you find Americans far away from their homes in the Solomon Islands. Between September 1, 1939 and September 2,1945, these two sides fought, both in Eastern Europe and in the Pacific, where Japanese forces attempted to control the Philippines, the Solomon Islands, and other territories, as strategic military bases. The Pacific Theater (theater = area of military operations) is where wartime messaging became particularly essential.

Navajo Code Talkers

A majority of eligible Native Americans enlisted in the military during WWII. Motivated by good jobs and fierce loyalty to the land, they made excellent soldiers who helped win the war.

Keeping information secret during war is serious business! Both the Allies and Axis made machines that encrypted messages, but even machines couldn't keep codes from being cracked. When a WWI veteran who spoke Navajo and English proposed using this complex language, the Marines recruited 29 Navajo men to create a code.

They also braved the battlefield, where fellow soldiers' lives depended on messages being translated in seconds. One thing that made the Navajo code so tough was that the language had never been written down. Enemy soldiers listening in had no way to know or look up what they were saying!

Chester Nez

Chester Nez was one of the 29 original Navajo Code Talkers. Although discouraged from using his native language in school, Nez used his knowledge of Navajo to develop a highly effective military code. He and other Navajo Soldiers were so successful at sending messages, the Marines recruited more than 300 men to this unit by the end of the war.

We remember Chester Nez especially because he shared his experience in his book, "Code Talker." In 2001, Nez received the Congressional Gold Medal for saving many lives and playing such an important role in United States history. Chester Nez was the last living Navajo Code Talker when he died in 2014 at the age of 93.

Can You Canoe?

Many Solomon Islanders sought to assist the Allied forces during the war as Coastwatchers. With over nine hundred islands, it was difficult to track the movement of enemy ships without having people radioing information about what they saw to a central headquarters. Sometimes this work was extremely dangerous, involving travel through hazardous waters and past enemy patrols.

One of the most famous adventures of Solomon Island coastal scouts happened in 1943, when an Australian coastwatcher saw an explosion from a crashed ship. While many thought the crew was lost, two Solomon Islanders took a canoe behind enemy lines and found a message the stranded crew had left behind. After a 38-mile journey avoiding ships and other dangers they got the information to the rest of the navy and the crew was rescued, including the future US President John F. Kennedy.

Can You Canoe?

Materials:

- Piece of paper
- Hot wax (or hot glue)
- Microwave Safe Container
- Paintbrush
- Microwave (You can also use a double boiler, but get help before using the stove)

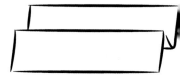

Directions:

1. Fold the piece of paper in half lengthwise

2. Fold each half of the paper again so that the paper makes a long M shape

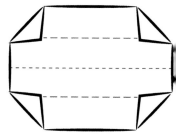

3. Unfold the paper and lay it flat. Fold each corner in to make a right triangle with the line from the closest fold.

4. With the corners folded in, fold the paper again inwards along the lines adjacent to the folded corners. This should put all the corners inside, and make a larger triangular shape where the folds are missing on each end.

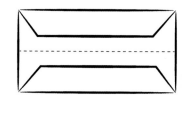

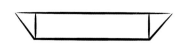

5. Fold along the center line to collapse those triangles. It will look like it did back in step 2, but you can feel on either end where your folds left a triangle shape where the paper is only two parts thick.

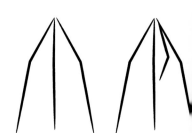

6. Take the corner of the folded paper which is less thick and fold it like you did the corners before. After you do this, unfold that corner and fold it the other direction. Unfold it again. This should leave a slightly creased fold in your paper.

7. Unfold the paper one step lengthwise. You should still have your edges folded inside.

8. **Place your finger at the tip of the triangle on one end, and pull the edges together while pushing up from the bottom. This should give you a canoe shape on one end. Repeat on the other end.**

9. Carefully tuck each end under one side of the center paper. You have completed your canoe!

10. Carefully melt the wax in the microwave by heating it for 2 and a half minutes, stirring it, then heating it another 2 and a half minutes. If it is not liquid yet, continue heating in half minute intervals.

11. Once your wax is melted, carefully use your paintbrush to apply a thin coat of wax to the bottom of your canoe. Avoid touching the wax, if you need to take a break and let a part cool down that's okay. Make sure to cover every inch, a single leak is a big problem!

12. Let your canoe sit for an hour, or until the wax dries.

13. It's time to test it out! Place your canoe carefully in water and watch it float.

Safety Tip:

Remember to be careful when doing this activity, and ask for a parents help! Hot wax can be dangerous if used incorrectly!

Know Your Navajo Culture

The Navajo, or the Diné, is the second largest Native American tribe in the United States. Diné means "the people" in the Navajo language.

The Navajo way of life is dependent on passing down important stories of how they came to be and how to live in the world. Stories were passed on through Navajo spoken language, songs, ceremonies, ritual, and prayer.

Navajo people were threatened by early colonizers, who tried to erase their language and culture. In 1864, about 12,000 Navajo were forced to walk over 300 miles from Arizona to New Mexico. During the "The Long Walk," almost 2,000 Navajo died.

Later, Navajo Assimilation Schools were set up to teach Navajo children the "American Way" of life. They weren't allowed to keep their native language or continue their traditional customs.

In spite of this and many other hardships, the Diné were and are a strong and resilient people. They believe that humans are connected with all entities on earth and in the universe—even bugs, dirt, stars, and clouds. An action cannot be taken without impacting everything and everyone.

> ***Say it like this:**
>
> **Hozho** - **"ho-ZHO"**
> The strongest syllable is always
> shown in **CAPITALS** and **red**.

To better understand the Navajo way of life, you have to understand Hozho*, way to live in harmony or "to walk in beauty." This key holistic concept is found in every aspect of Navajo language, art, and culture, including this traditional Navajo prayer:

As I walk, as I walk The universe is walking with me
In beauty it walks before me In beauty it walks behind me
In beauty it walks below me In beauty it walks above me
Beauty is on every side As I walk, I walk with Beauty.

How might your worldview change if you woke up every day repeating these words?

_____

_____

_____

_____

_____

_____

_____

_____

Know Your Maps

Are We There Yet?

Maps are designed to help us navigate our surroundings. During WWII, maps were printed on cloth handkerchiefs. Soldiers tucked these inside the heels of their boots, in case they needed to escape from danger. Just like maps were used to find safety during war, maps of our brain can help us better understand our bodies and keep them healthy and safe.

With an MRI (magnetic resonance* imaging), we can see a map of neural activity based on where the brain has the most blood flow. Scientists can also map neural pathways through parts of the brain which communicate with each other. With over 100 trillion connections between neurons in the human brain, that's quite a map! This complex map is called a connectome.* It's your brain's record of thoughts, knowledge, skills and memories. In fact, every time you learn something, connections (pathways in your connectome) grow and can grow stronger.

Besides maps of brain activity and structure, there are mind maps (a diagram where you chart out ideas) and movement maps (a set of steps on how to perform an action—for example, riding a bike, doing a cartwheel, or frying an egg).

Know Your Geography: Guadalcanal

Look at a map of the Solomon Islands. Where is Guadalcanal? Why would the U.S. and Japan both want Guadalcanal as a military base?

Guadalcanal was strategically located: far enough from Japan, but close enough to the United States and Australia. From here, Japanese airplanes could easily reach either coast.

The U.S. and Japan battled over Guadalcanal for months. Both sides lost many ships, aircraft, resources, and troops. In 1943, the Japanese evacuated* the island. The U.S. took control of Guadalcanal, and, soon, other islands in the South Pacific.

In 1976, the Solomon Islands became self-governing, and in 1978, gained independence.

Having a map—any kind of map—gives you information and options. They tell you where things are, and help you find where you're going and how you can get there. Brains and maps go hand-in-hand!

*Say it like this:

resonance - "**REZ**-uh-nince"

connectome - "ku-**NECK**-tome"

evacuated - "ee-**VAH**-kyoo-ate-ted"

The strongest syllable is alwa shown in **CAPITALS** and **red**.

Know Your Codes

I Saw the Sign

When your brain sends a message to your peripheral nervous system, it's important that information is clear. From headquarters to the front lines, signals have to be fast, direct, and accurate.

The Navajo language made a very effective code. Navajo Code Talkers developed code words using different methods, sometimes translating specific terms, or spelling words they didn't already have coded. Animals were often used to represent both letters and terms. Mosai (cat) was code for the letter "C," while atsa (eagle) was code for a transport plane.

Other codes are swirling all around us—from the satellites floating in space to the barcodes on our cereal boxes to binary code in computers! When pilots land planes, the ground crew communicates with them visually using flag semaphore (you probably guessed it—a code where flags represent letters!).

*Founded in 1949, NATO stands for "North Atlantic Treaty Organization." Its purpose is to protect the freedom & security of its members, which include Canada, France, the U.S. and 25 other nations.

Let's learn two simple codes: Morse and the NATO* alphabet.

It's in code!

NATO Alphabet Key

A Alpha	**G** Golf	**M** Mike	**S** Sierra	**Y** Yankee
B Bravo	**H** Hotel	**N** November	**T** Tango	**Z** Zulu
C Charlie	**I** India	**O** Oscar	**U** Uniform	
D Delta	**J** Juliet	**P** Papa	**V** Victor	
E Echo	**K** Kilo	**Q** Quebec	**W** Whiskey	
F Foxtrot	**L** Lima	**R** Romeo	**X** X-ray	

The NATO alphabet was created for clear communication over radio and telephone. Twenty-six words are assigned to each letter of the English alphabet. Instead of wondering if B sounds like P or T, you can say Bravo, Papa, or Tango. No confusion!

Transmitted by light or sound, Morse code uses combinations of short and long signals to represent the alphabet. The most famous Morse code message is S-O-S, the international sign for distress. It's conveyed by 3 short, 3 long, 3 short flashes/beeps.

Now grab a friend and your flashlight—it's time to send some messages!

I Put A Spell On You

Materials:

- Flashlight
- A Friend
- Morse Code Key (right)

Directions:

1. Copy the Morse code key, including punctuation, so you and your friend both have one.

2. Stand across from your friend in a dark place, like a room with the lights off or outside after the sun has started to set.

3. Using Morse code, transmit the following messages (or make up your own) and see if your friend can figure them out. Note that • is a short signal, – is a long signal (about 3 times longer than •).

4. How hard was that? Now let your friend send new messages while you receive them.

5. **Extra challenge:** Try Morse code with sound. Use your whistle instead of your light. **Is that easier?**

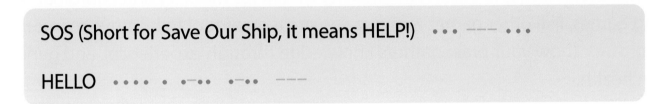

SOS (Short for Save Our Ship, it means HELP!) ••• ——— •••

HELLO •••• • •—•• •—•• ———

Can you figure out the next two?

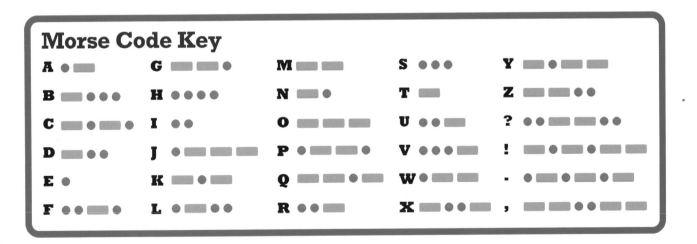

WANT PIZZA

LOL

Morse Code Key

A •■	G ■■•	M ■■	S •••	Y ■•■■
B ■•••	H ••••	N ■•	T ■	Z ■■••
C ■•■•	I ••	O ■■■	U ••■	? ••■■••
D ■••	J •■■■	P •■■•	V •••■	! ■•■•■■
E •	K ■•■	Q ■■•■	W •■■	- •■■■■•
F ••■•	L •■••	R ••■	X ■••■	, ■■••■■

Know More Na'atl'o!

Navajo String Games

You might already know a popular string game: Cat's Cradle! The Navajo have string games that make shapes from nature and everyday life, such as coyotes, butterflies, baskets, and stars. A fun activity that helps mobility and coordination, string games, like other games and puzzles, are a great tool to improve memory, cognition* (how your brain gathers knowledge through experience), and general brain health.

Just as we exercise to become faster and stronger, we exercise our brain with new or challenging tasks. Brain exercise can even increase gray matter, the "thinking" portion of the brain. It's involved in everything from muscle control to sensory perception. Growing your gray matter means a stronger brain, and the better your ability to remember your homework.

*Say it like this:

cognition - "cog-NIH-shun"

astrocyte - "A-struh-site"

The strongest syllable is always shown in **CAPITALS** and **red**.

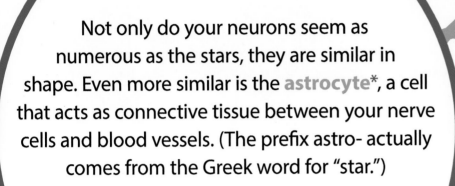

Not only do your neurons seem as numerous as the stars, they are similar in shape. Even more similar is the astrocyte*, a cell that acts as connective tissue between your nerve cells and blood vessels. (The prefix astro- actually comes from the Greek word for "star.")

Try the string game below, known by the Navajo as "simple star."

BRAIN FLASH
String games use the portion of your brain that processes mathematical thought.

I've Got the World on a String

Materials:

- Yarn
- 2 hands
- 1 brain
- Lots of patience and practice

Directions:

1. Your string is an endless loop, an "O." Wrap it around your pointer finger and thumb on both hands, just like in Figure 1.

2. With your right thumb and pointer, grab and twist the part of the string on your left hand. See the teal section in Figure 2.

3. As you twist, slip your right pointer and thumb into the string. You'll end up with two strands on your right hand (Figure 3).

4. Repeat this move with your left thumb and pointer. Go under the top string on your right hand, then grab and twist the bottom strand. Your goal is an "X" shape like in Figure 4. (Note the strands in teal—they're the next to move.)

5. Swoop both pinkies under the top strands on your thumbs.

6. Spread both hands wide. You should have loops around both pinkies (Figure 6).

7. Bring your hands a little closer together so the whole string softens. Carefully drop both thumbs out of the string (Figure 7).

8. See the strands looped over both pointers? Slip each thumb into the loop above it (Figure 8).

9. Spread your hands wide. You should see a star! Besides yourself.

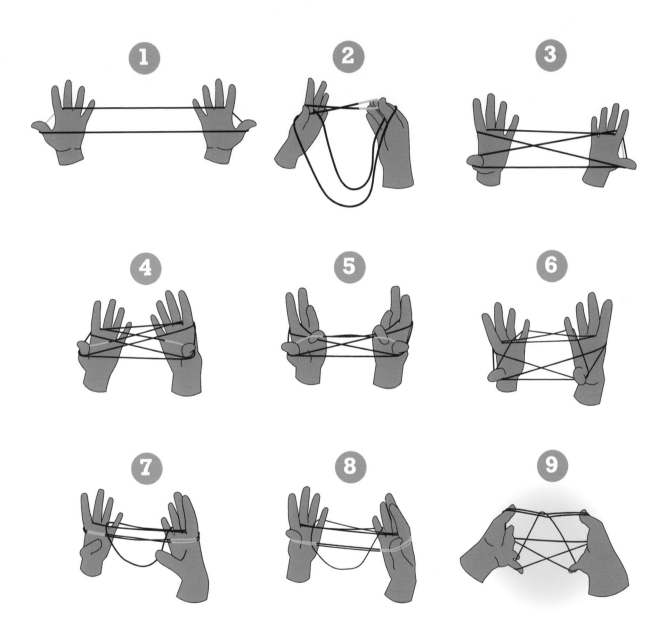

Solomon Island Secrets

After you finish, check the answer key on page 106.

Across:

1. A complex language that helped America create an unbreakable communication code during WWII

5. The abbreviation for a global war involving the Allies and the Axis

7. A key holistic concept found in Navajo language, art, and culture

8. Made up of more than nine hundred islands

Down:

2. Type of school that forced Navajo to learn the "American Way"

3. A Native American who received a Congressional Gold Medal for his role in United States History

4. Translation of Yá'át'ééh in Navajo

6. An area of military operations during WWII

9. Means "the people" in Navajo language

Crack the Code

Good work, Adventurers!

Now that you have read some things about the Solomon Islands, let's review what you have learned!

Fill in the blanks.

The Second World War involved over __ __ __ __ __ __ countries in a conflict mainly between the __ __ __ __ __ __ and the __ __ __ __. These two sides fought on two fronts, one in Europe and the other in the __ __ __ __ __ __ __ , where the Solomon Islands became a fierce battleground. One the of the essential features of that theater was wartime __ __ __ __ __ __ __ __ .

Many __ __ __ __ __ __ Americans enlisted in the military during WWII due to their loyalty to the __ __ __ __ . Using a strategy developed in the first World War, the Marines recruited 29 men from the __ __ __ __ __ __ to create a code using their complex language that had never been __ __ __ __ __ __ __ down to help keep messages both secret and easily translated. This code was so effective the Marines recruited more than __ __ __ Code Talkers by the end of the war.

You can check your answers using the key on page 110.

While the United States appreciated the Navajo in WWII, this was not always the case. In 1864, __ __ ,__ __ __ Navajo were forced to walk from Arizona to New Mexico, and almost __, __ __ __ died on the journey. Schools were set up to teach Navajo children the " __ __ __ __ __ __ __ __ __ __ __ " of life to try and eliminate their culture.

The Navajo, or __ __ __ __ __ __ __, survived this and held on to their belief that everyone and everything is connected. Their belief called the __ __ __ __ __ teaches one "to walk in __ __ __ __ __ __" and is found deeply entwined in their culture.

Know Your Nervous System

The coolest thing about the nervous system is that this system is you! It senses what is happening in your world and sends signals to activate other parts of your body in response to what it senses. Everything you think, feel, and do happens because of your nervous system.

Your nervous system is made up of the **central nervous system**—your brain and spinal cord — and the **peripheral nervous system**—all the nerves that branch off of the brain (cranial nerves) and spinal cord (spinal nerves) and run throughout your body relaying messages to and from the brain.

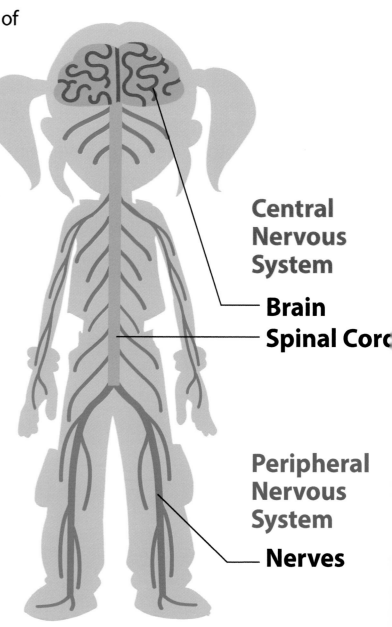

Central Nervous System

Brain
Spinal Cord

Peripheral Nervous System

Nerves

Gray Matter Matters

If your body is an army, your brain is the commander— it receives information, interprets it, and sends orders to the rest of your body based on that information. Your complex brain isn't just a single glob of tissue. It has three main parts: the cerebrum, the cerebellum, and the brain stem, and each one serves a different function.

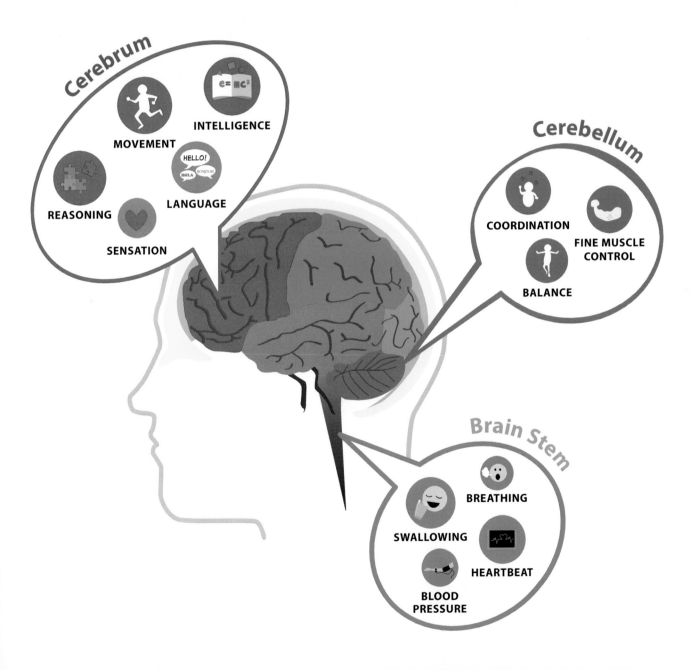

Know Your Nervous System

The cerebrum is the largest part of your brain and controls your thoughts and voluntary motor functions. Your thoughts include everything you think about: what you want for dinner, the lyrics to your favorite song, or how to solve a tricky math problem. Your voluntary motor functions are the movements your body has to think about: jumping rope, playing the harmonica, or flicking a mosquito off your arm.

Your cerebellum sits underneath your cerebrum in the back of your brain. It's smaller than your cerebrum, but is incredibly important. It controls your balance and posture, so you can sit, stand, and walk without falling over. While your cerebrum tells your body to move, your cerebellum tells your body how to move by instructing different muscle groups to work together.

Your brain stem, even smaller than the cerebellum, keeps you alive. It controls the activities you don't think about: swallowing, breathing, digestion, blood circulation, and heartbeat. It even controls whether you're awake or feeling sleepy.

Know Your Nervous System

The Power of Lobe

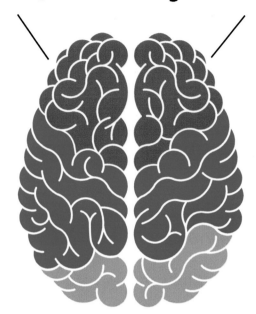

Left Hemisphere   **Right Hemisphere**

Your cerebrum is divided into two hemispheres, left and right, and they work in a surprising way. The left hemisphere actually controls the right side of your body, while the right hemisphere controls the left side of your body!

Each hemisphere is divided into four lobes, and each lobe controls a specific function:

- The frontal lobe controls emotions and behavior. It lets you reason and plan for the future, and controls certain aspects of your speech and movements.

- The parietal* lobe processes a lot of the information you sense through touch, like temperature, pressure, and pain, as well as what you taste.

- The occipital* lobe is the part of the brain most responsible for vision.

- The temporal* lobe deals with the information you hear, including speech. It also processes your memories.

---

* Say it like this:

Parietal - "pa-RIOT-al"   **Occipital** - "ox-SIP-it-al"

Temporal - "tem-PER-al"

The strongest syllable is always shown in **CAPITALS** and **red**.

How do we know what part of the brain controls what? Well, there are a few ways. If someone injures their brain and loses the ability to speak, we know that the part of the brain they damaged somehow controls speech. Fortunately, there are less painful ways to learn about the brain. Technologies like PET scans and functional MRIs see which parts of the brain are working while we perform different tasks.

There's still so much we don't know about the brain. We're always learning new things about the ways it works—expanding our own brains in the process.

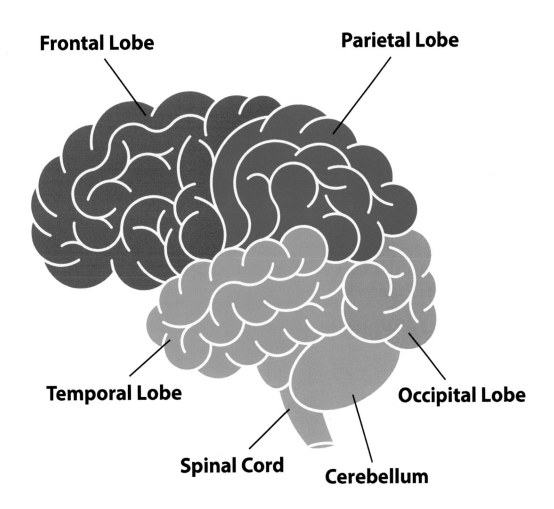

Frontal Lobe

Parietal Lobe

Temporal Lobe

Occipital Lobe

Spinal Cord

Cerebellum

A-MAZE-ing Brain

In this guide, you learned about central and peripheral nervous systems, which use your brain, spinal cord, and neurons to carry messages throughout your body. Now that you've gotten to know your nervous system, you might think your brain is pretty a-MAZE-ing!

Travel through the central nervous system, neuron style, to complete the brain maze! Afterwards, can you help Pinky unscramble the names of the nervous system?

Materials:

- Pencil

Directions:

1. Starting at the up arrow, find your way through the brain maze!
2. Fill in the blanks to label each part of the brain.

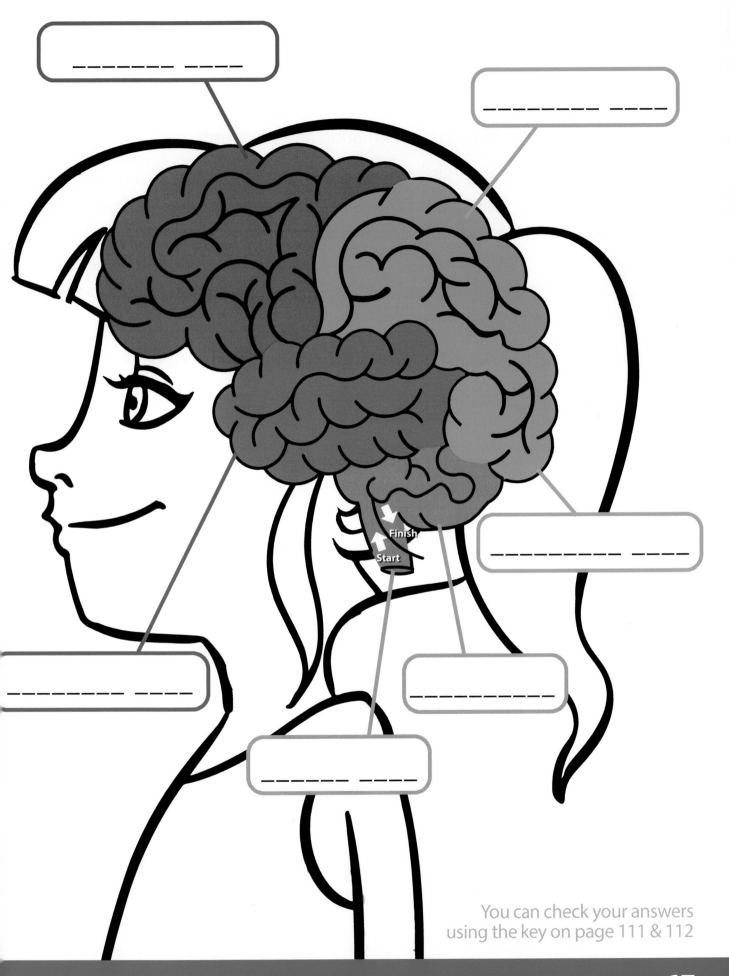

You can check your answers
using the key on page 111 & 112

Know Your Neurons

Your powerful and complex brain can't do everything alone. A commander needs special troops to gather information and issue orders.

Your body has millions of cells, called **neurons**, these neurons come together to form nerves that branch out from your spinal cord to the rest of the body. The neurons in your spinal cord connect with neurons in your brain to be able to send information back and forth to one another. Imagine these nerves extending throughout your whole body as a very fast information transportation highway.

All neurons send messages between the body and brain, but different neurons send those messages in different directions:

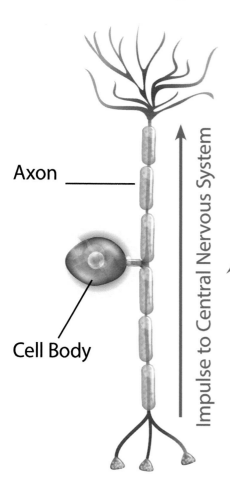

Axon

Cell Body

Impulse to Central Nervous System

Sensory neurons are the body's recon team. They take information from the eyes, nose, and other sensory organs and send it to the brain. There are four different kinds of sensory neurons that react to different input:

- **Thermoreceptors** react to changes in temperature.
- **Photoreceptors** react to light.
- **Chemoreceptors** react to chemical changes, like in the taste buds or nose.
- **Baroreceptors** react to pressure, touch, and vibration.

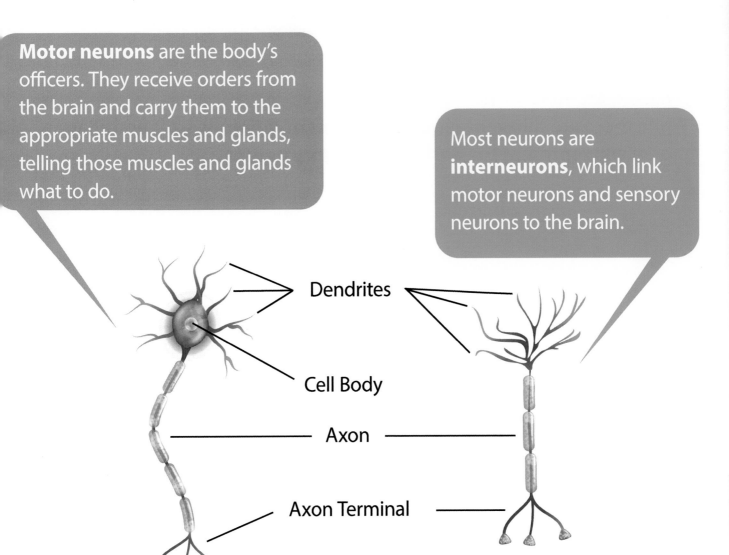

Motor neurons are the body's officers. They receive orders from the brain and carry them to the appropriate muscles and glands, telling those muscles and glands what to do.

Most neurons are **interneurons**, which link motor neurons and sensory neurons to the brain.

Dendrites

Cell Body

Axon

Axon Terminal

The Electric Slide...or Hop?

The transfer of signals is both electrical (within neurons) and chemical (across neurons)! From the **dendrite** (the branch-like structure that receives signals), down the **axon** (the neuron's electrical cable), to the ends of the axon (sometimes called the axon terminal), the signal has to jump over a tiny gap between axon terminal and dendrite.

This gap where signals connect is called a **synapse**. These connections are how messages hop from neuron to neuron until they get where they need to go.

Need for Neurons

While there are different types of neurons of different sizes and shapes, this model will represent the basics of a sensory neuron.

There's no better way to understand the makeup of a neuron than by making one yourself.

Materials:

- 3 colors of playdough (See "Making Materials" to make your own)
- Flat, clean space for rolling
- Ruler or measuring tape

Directions:

1. Take one of your playdough colors. Roll one piece that is as small around as you can get it without it breaking and about four inches long This will be the center of your axon.

2. Roll three smaller pieces one half inch long and attach them at the bottom of your axon. These represent your axon terminals.

3. At the top of the axon, make a variety of short lengths to be your nerve endings. It should look like the branches of a tree spreading out.

4. Taking your second color, make an oval about an inch long. This is your cell body, or 'soma.' Place it aside for now.

5. Take your third color of dough. Use it to form flat pieces about a half inch wide. Take these pieces and wrap them around the long section of your axon that you made first, leaving a bit of space between each covering. This is your myelin sheath. Using a bit of the third color, attach the cell body to the side of the center of your axon.

6. Compare your neuron to the pictures in Know Your Neurons.

Can you figure out how to make the other neurons?

Making Materials

Need for Neurons

Materials:

- 2 cups all-purpose flour
- ¾ cup salt
- 4 teaspoons cream of tartar
- 2 cups room temperature water
- 2 tablespoons vegetable or coconut oil
- 3 colors of food coloring (Red, Yellow and Green work well)
- 1 large pot
- 3 quart sized bags

Pinky's Safety Tip:

Remember to be careful when doing this activity, and ask for a parents help! A hot stove can be dangerous if used incorrectly!

Directions:

1. Put flour, salt and cream of tartar in a large pot and stir until mixed.

2. Add water and oil and stir together.

3. Cook the mix on the stove over medium heat, stirring constantly until it starts to thicken. It should begin to start forming into a ball like shape when it's done.

4. Remove from heat, and carefully place on wax paper to cool until it's safe to touch.

5. Take your ball of dough and knead it together until it becomes smooth.

6. Divide the ball into three sections, and put them in separate bags.

7. Add about 5 drops of food coloring to each bag, then close the bags and knead the bags until the dough is colored. After it's mixed, remove the now colored dough and let it dry a bit.

8.. Use your dough to make models of each of the three types of neuron in "Need a Neuron" or for any other exciting adventure.

Dome Sweet Dome

Remember your cranial nerves?
They have names (they're a mouthful,
so we included a pronunciation guide).
Look at the list of nerves below, then match
the activities to the correct nerve. By doing these
movements, you're learning—and creating neural
connections in your brain. By getting to know
your brain better, you're expanding the map of
your brain!

Hint: Some activities might match
more than one nerve.

Without moving your head, look at the ceiling.

Smile, frown, furrow your brows.

Shake your head "no."

Stick out your tongue.

Look at a sign from far away.

Eat a few bites of a snack.

Cover one eye. Can you see as well with your right eye as your left?

Listen to your favorite song. Try to stand on one leg for a count of 10.

Jump up and down 10 times, or until your feel your heart beat a bit faster.

Take a deep sniff of your favorite smell: cinnamon, mint, pine trees.

Look down at your nose.

Say a sentence out loud.

Look left and right without turning your head.

1 Olfactory (ol-fak-tuh-ree) <u>Smell</u>.

2 Optic (op-tik) <u>Vision</u>.

3 Oculomotor (awk-you-low-mo-tor) Moving eyes up, down, toward your center. <u>Moving eyelids</u>.

4 Trochlear (troke-lee-ur) <u>Moving eyes down and in</u>.

5 Trigeminal (tri-gem-ih-null) Sensations of the face. <u>Chewing and biting</u>. Its name means 3x twins—each side of this nerve has three branches!

6 Abducens (ab-doo-senz) <u>Moving eyes away from center</u>. Abduct = to take away.

7 Facial (fay-shull) <u>Taste, expression, and facial and scalp movements</u>.

8 Vestibulolcochlear (ves-ti-byoo-lo-coke-lee-ur) <u>Hearing and balance</u>.

9 Glossopharyngeal (gloss-o-fah-ringe-ee-uhl) Sensory and motor. <u>Taste, throat, swallowing</u>.

10 Vagus (vay-gus) <u>Throat, voice, coughing; glands, digestion, heart rate, respiration</u>.

11 Accessory (ak-cess-uh-ree) <u>Rotating head, shrugging shoulders, raising chin</u>.

12 Hypoglossal (hi-po-gloss-uhl) <u>Moving your tongue</u>.

You can check your answers using the key on page 114.

Know Your Fears

You already know the brain can change with physical injury.

A hit to the head can cause a concussion, resulting in the brain shaking inside the skull. **Ouch!** You could experience pain, emotional imbalance, and problems with memory, sleep, and other brain functions.

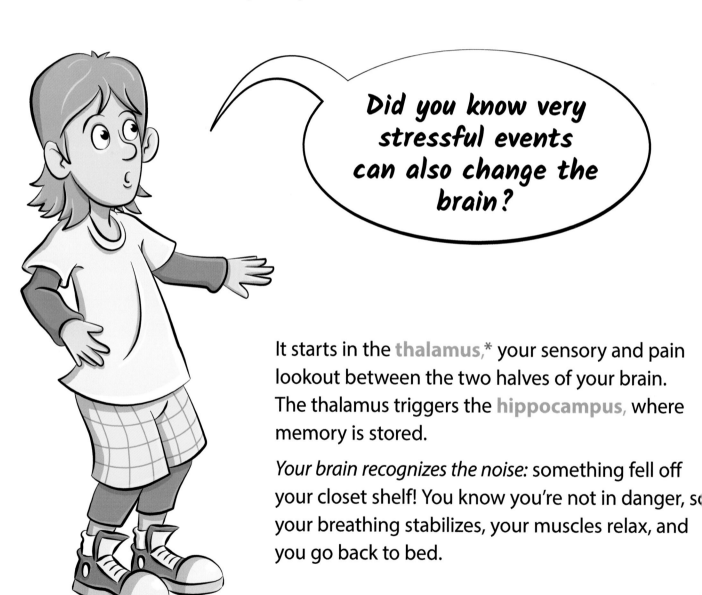

Did you know very stressful events can also change the brain?

It starts in the thalamus,* your sensory and pain lookout between the two halves of your brain. The thalamus triggers the hippocampus, where memory is stored.

Your brain recognizes the noise: something fell off your closet shelf! You know you're not in danger, so your breathing stabilizes, your muscles relax, and you go back to bed.

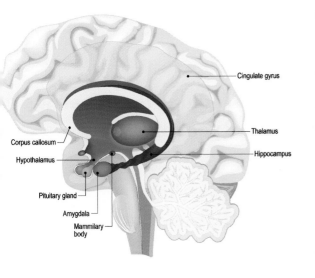

Cingulate gyrus

Thalamus

Hippocampus

Corpus callosum

Hypothalamus

Pituitary gland

Amygdala

Mammilary body

What if your closet door swings open and a *big orange swamp monster* jumps out? Your thalamus alerts the amygdala*, a small almond-shaped set of neurons where you feel emotion. The amygdala signals the hypothalamus, which triggers the release of stress hormones. This sends blood to your muscles so you can fight that monster!

Sometimes this process doesn't work the way it was designed. While we want our bodies to react to danger this state is supposed to be temporary. Sometimes our brains can react, even if it might not need to.

Trauma* is an event outside of normal experience—such as a car accident, a fight, or an injury. Trauma is so stressful, it changes the brain so fight or flight is not temporary but happens whenever the traumatic memory is triggered.

When a traumatic memory is triggered, cell memories tell the body to react as if anything were as dangerous as bombs, causing anxiety, sleeplessness, rage, shaking, illness, depression, or other symptoms. This is known as Post Traumatic Stress Disorder, or PTSD.

Remember: If something has given you feelings of fear or anxiety, that's part of being a person. Learning how to deal with these feelings is important for your body and mind.

*Say them like this:

thalmus - "THA-luh-muss"   **amygdala** -"THA-luh-muss"

trauma - "TRAW-muh"

The strongest syllable is always shown in CAPITALS and red.

Peace by Piece

It's normal to feel fear, anxiety, and stress. Acknowledging these feelings can prevent them from wreaking havoc on you and your brain.

First, pay attention to your body and learn the physical signs that you're feeling afraid or anxious. These signs can help you bring your fear to the surface.

Do you sweat or start shaking?

Does it seem hard to breathe?

Your nervous system wants to make sure you're safe, so think about some of the things your "emotional first aid kit" should have.

Here are some ideas to get you started:

Emotional First Aid Kit

- ✚ People you trust
- ✚ Your pets
- ✚ Activites you enjoy
- ✚ "Fidgets" like putty

- ✚ Writing notes to yourself
- ✚ Your favorite music
- ✚ Exercise
- ✚ Rest

Your pack may have different items, and that is okay! Your fears are unique, just like you. Remember to put it together when you are not feeling scared or anxious, so that it is ready for when you need it. **The most important thing is that you can look for help to face things that scare you.**

What if you had an emotional guardian for your nervous system? Think of it as a sort of first aid kit—a pack to both protect you and help you recover.

Feeling and Dealing

Where anatomy, physiology, and psychology all come together

You might not have realized during all the excitement in the comic that everyone—the Loops Crew, Chester, even you—was responding to stress.

Did you know that stress can sometimes be a good thing?

Good stress—the kind that can improve your well-being—is eustress.* Think of eustress as a satisfying challenge, like graduation day, or a big performance or game. Eustress is normal, and actually beneficial.

Bad Stress or Distress,* however, is considered a threat by your nervous system: situations of danger, fear, or anxiety, but also scarcity, like not getting enough sleep, food, or water.

*Say them like this:

eustress - "YOU-stress"

distress - "dih-STRESS"

homeostasis - "home-ee-oh-STAY-sis"

The strongest syllable is always shown in **CAPITALS** and **red**.

The **sympathetic nervous system** (SNS) responds to stress of all kinds. It responds to non-threatening stress the same way it does when fighting for survival. Too much distress can cause the body to feel like it's always fighting for its life—that's a problem!

Luckily, the sympathetic nervous system has a very best friend: the **parasympathetic nervous system** (PSNS). While the SNS goes for fight or flight, calm and collected PSNS says rest and digest. Once the SNS makes sure we're safe, the PSNS helps us recuperate. Both are important!

Like any good tag team, both these systems work together for that life-saving balance called **homeostasis**.*

If you find you are experiencing more distress than eustress, try this PSNS Training Guide:

1 Dance or go for a walk.

2 Nap, read, or meditate.

3 Spend time with a loved one or friend.

Know Your Nervous System

BARORECEPTOR

BRAINSTEM

CENTRAL

CEREBELLUM

CEREBRUM

CHEMORECEPTOR

FRONTAL

LOBE

NEURON

OCCIPITAL

PARIETAL

PERIPHERAL

PHOTORECEPTOR

TEMPORAL

THERMORECEPT

Answer keys on page 107

```
O J X O B A R O R E C E P T O R A P
C D G A W M W X T E M P O R A L V A
C D E C E N T R A L R I R Y I G C R
I P H O T O R E C E P T O R U Z E I
P J A W R C N E F R O N T A L C R E
I S Q G N C E R E B E L L U M Y E T
T O L S H E O I V M N G A F H L B A
A P E R I P H E R A L B V E T O R L
L C H E M O R E C E P T O R T B U V
Q T H E R M O R E C E P T O R E M J
I I N T C X B R A I N S T E M F L B
W J P I E N E U R O N Z N A Q I N M
```

Brain Bop!

Information Review

Good work, Adventurers! Now that you know the nervous system, let's review what you've learned!

Try to fill in the blanks.

The nervous system is __ __ __ ! The way it works is by sensing what is happening outside your body and sending __ __ __ __ __ __ __ to other parts inside your body about how to act in response. Your __ __ __ __ __ __ __ nervous system is made up of your brain and spinal cord.

The __ __ __ __ __ __ __ __ __ __ nervous system is composed of all the nerves branching from your spinal cord and throughout your body.

In the body, your brain plays the part of __ __ __ __ __ __ __ __ __, receiving and interpreting information, and then sending out orders to the rest of the body.

The three main parts of the brain are the __ __ __ __ __ __ __ __ , cerebellum, and brain __ __ __ __. The cerebrum is responsible for thoughts and __ __ __ __ __ __ __ __ __ __ motor functions.

The __ __ __ __ __ __ __ __ __ __ __ is the part in charge of balance and posture. The brain stem helps keep you alive by controlling the activities you don't think about - for example, involuntary activities like __ __ __ __ __ __ __ __ __ and swallowing.

Your brain uses millions of nerve cells, called __ __ __ __ __ __ __, that form long chains branching out from your spinal cord and to the rest of your body. These important cells help send messages between the body and __ __ __ __ __ __. The three types of neurons are called __ __ __ __ __ __ __ __ neurons, __ __ __ __ __ __ neurons, and interneurons.

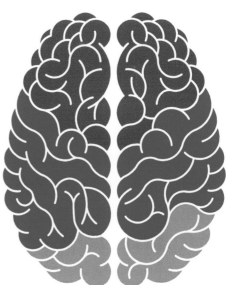

Ready to verify what you have learned? See the answer key on page 110.

Know Your Appetite

Food, Glorious Fuel

Your body needs nourishment to live. Your brain (working even while you sleep) is no exception, using about 20% of the calories you eat. It loves good food— fuel to keep your nervous system running!

Our relationship to food has changed over time. We used to hunt and farm instead of going to the store. Native Americans, for example, originally lived off the land: bison, berries, herbs. They grew vegetables and raised animals—and all of it organic!

In the 1880s, indigenous people were forced to leave their land, move to reservations, and replace their traditional food with items such as wheat flour, sugar, and dairy. The bison had been hunted to near extinction and harsh living conditions on the reservation made farming difficult. Chester Nez touches on this in his memoir, "Code Talker," when he talks about how much he and the other Navajo Marines loved their meals in boot camp. To them, the food was plentiful and delicious!

In World War 2 (WWII), it was part of the war effort to maintain rations for soldiers abroad. People were encouraged to plant and harvest their own fruits and vegetables—something the indigenous tribes were already used to doing.

Pinky's Hint:

Read through the entire recipe. This way, you'll know what equipment and ingredients are needed, and you'll be familiar with the steps involved.

 Whenever you see the chef's hat icon, it means **you'll need an adult's help**.

Dichin nisin!

That means
"I feel hungry"
in Navajo.

**Recipes and food knowledge provided by
Chef Polly Legendre of La Gourmande Catering.**

*Say it like this:

Dichin nisin - **"deh-CHIN-n-sin"**

The strongest syllable is always
shown in **CAPITALS** and **red**.

WWII Victory Garden Salad

In World War I (WWI), the American government encouraged people to plant their own food. "Victory Gardens" ensured there was enough to send the troops, as well as prevent a food shortage back home. Just as popular in WWII, these gardens were planted in backyards, in window boxes, on apartment rooftops, or in public parks. Many schools planted their own tomatoes, lettuce, and peas and used them in school lunches. Most people ate produce that was locally grown, saving trains and trucks to transport supplies and soldiers.

Twenty million families grew gardens in 1943. By 1944, Victory Gardens were producing 40 percent of the vegetables in United States! No matter where they were planted, Victory Gardens sent the same message: this food was being grown by the people, for the people.

Ingredients:

Prep time: 20 minutes
Serves 4-6

- 1 cup cherry tomatoes
- 1 bunch spring onions
- 1 cup green beans
- 2 cups cauliflower flowerets
- 1 small bunch of baby broccoli (optional)
- 1 cup corn (optional)
- 1 cup green peas (optional)

Feel free to add other vegetables like cabbage, beets, carrots or red onion!

Preparation:

1. If using cauliflower, broccoli, corn, peas, or green beans, steam the vegetables until they are just tender.
Let them cool.

2. Mix all the vegetables in a large bowl and toss with the mustard dressing (see below). Ready to serve!

Mustard Salad Dressing

- 2 tbsp vinegar
- 1/8 tsp salt
- 2 tbsp mustard
- 1/2 cup olive or vegetable oil
- Fresh ground pepper
- A jar (with a lid!)

1. Place all ingredients in a covered jar, shake vigorously to blend.

Show off your cooking skills!

Have your grown up take a photo, and share on social media using the hashtag:

#KnowYourAdventure

 KnowYourselfOAK   KnowYourselfOAK

Cottage Cheese & Green Onion Muffins

Prep time:
20-30 minutes

Cooking time:
18 to 20 minutes

Serves
6 people

Ingredients:

- 1-3/4 cup flour
- 1 tsp sugar
- 2 tsp baking powder
- 1/2 tsp salt
- 1 cup cottage cheese
- ½ cup milk
- 3 tbsp vegetable oil
- ½ cup chopped green onions
- 1 egg

Preparation:

1. Preheat the oven to 375 degrees. Line 12 regular size muffin cups with paper liners, or spray with cooking spray.

2. In a large bowl, mix the flour, sugar, baking powder, and salt until well blended.

3. In another large bowl, beat the cottage cheese, milk, vegetable oil, onions, and egg with wire whisk until well blended.

4. Pour the wet ingredients over the dry ingredients. Fold in only until all ingredients are moistened.

5. Spoon the batter evenly into the muffin cups, just below full. Bake for 18–20 minutes or until golden brown and a toothpick inserted in the center comes out clean. Serve warm. 👨‍🍳

Thoughts for Young Chefs

Cooking is an important skill. It's key to how we nourish ourselves and others. Besides making delicious food, **what else do you learn when you cook?**

_____

_____

_____

_____

Know Yourself Adventure Recipes

Review the recipes from previous Adventures and choose a destination to compare. Record similarities and differences in the Venn Diagram below.

Similarities   **Differences**

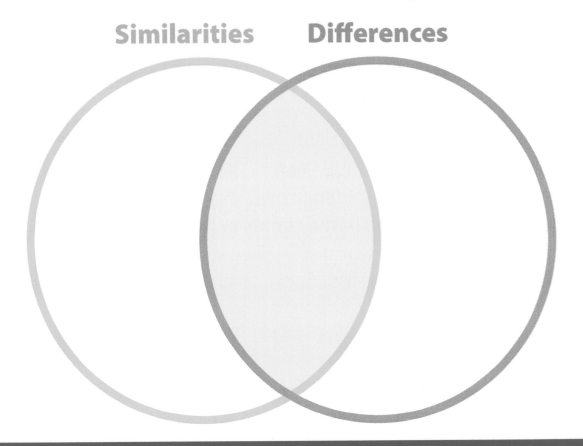

a recipe calls for 1 cup of milk and you only have a ½ cup measuring cup, what
an you do to measure out 1 cup? What if you only have ¼ cup? Or a ⅓ cup? Or a ¾
up?

_____

_____

_____

f you need a tablespoon of salt (often written as "tbsp") and you only have a
easpoon (often written as "tsp") to measure, **what do you do?**

_____

_____

_____

ry doubling the Cottage Cheese & Green Onion Muffin recipe on page 20 to make
wice as many muffins. **What do you have to figure out?**

_____

_____

_____

_____

Thoughts for Young Chefs

Make the Cottage Cheese & Green Onion Muffins according to the recipe. Then make the same muffins, but change one ingredient: use 2½ tbsp of butter instead of 3 tbsp of vegetable oil, or use 1 cup of ricotta cheese instead of 1 cup of cottage cheese.

- **Do the muffins taste different?**
- **Do they have a different shape or consistency?**
- **What do you think causes those differences to happen?**
- **What did you learn from changing the ingredients?**

_____

_____

_____

_____

_____

_____

_____

What's the difference between slice, chop, mince, and grate? **Why do you think it matters how an ingredient is cut up before it's cooked?**

_____

_____

_____

Cooking, like any skill, requires patience, time, and practice. While gaining culinary know-how, you also get a chance to use a bit of math and science in the process!

Bonus: Talk with someone you know who had a different food experience growing up.
Did they live through the food rationing of the 1940s, or grow up in a different country? **How did this experience shape the way they think of food now?**

_____

_____

_____

_____

_____

_____

_____

Epic Brainpower

In this Adventure, you learned about the nervous system and how your brain controls the way you operate.

What are some ways that you use your nervous system everyday?

_____

_____

_____

_____

_____

_____

_____

_____

_____

eady to make new pathways in your brain? Try this brain break and answer the
uesitons below.

tart by making a fist with both of your hands. In one hand extend your pointer
nger, on the other extend your pinky. Now try switching, and repeat 6 times.

**Were you able to do it on your first try? If not, come back in a few weeks but
eep trying see how it compares to when you first started!**

_____

_____

_____

_____

_____

_____

_____

_____

_____

Further Reading

History Resources

Nonfiction

This book is filled with beautiful and detailed photographs, dimensional imagery, and paired with further reading to grow readers' curiosity about the brain. Seymour Simon is an award-winning author of children's science literature

Simon, Seymour. **The Brain: All about our Nervous System and More!** HaperCollins Publishers, 2007. (Ages 6+)

This is a great starting point for kids interested in learning more about the brain and nervous system. KidsHealth empowers families by providing doctor-reviewed material on a variety of topics with parents, kids, and teens in mind.

"Your Brain & Nervous System." KidsHealth, retrieved Mar. 2021 https://kidshealth.org/en/kids/brain.html?WT.ac=p-ra (Age 10+)

Fiction

For those interested in learning more about the Navajo, this book elegantly retells the Navajo legend about the mysteries of the stars. The story and illustrations capture both a desire to understand and an appreciation of natural beauty.

Oughton, Jerrie. **How the Stars Fell Into the Sky: A Navajo Legend.** United Kingdom, Houghton Mifflin, 1996. (Ages 5+)

Based on the stories of Code Talkers in both WW1 and WW2, this graphic novel tells seven stories about code talkers from multiple Native tribes. It includes both exciting depictions based on true stories as well as nonfiction material to delve further into the details.

Tales of the Mighty Code Talkers. United States, Native Realities LLC, 2016 (Ages 12+)

NEXT
The Integumentary System

KN🔍W YOURSELF

12

The Integumentary System
If I Could Derm Back Time

Lucille's

OAKLAND

Run your hands through your hair, and learn about it like you just don't care! **Finish off this adventure where it all started in The United States. The year is 1967** and Shorty Lemonade's great great grandmother is waiting for you to help you learn about the integumentary system.

Yeah! Run your hands through your hair, and learn about it like you just don't care! Finish off this adventure where it all started, in **The United States. The year is 1967** and Shorty Lemonade's great great grandmother is waiting for you. Learn about the integumentary system in . . . **If I Could Derm Back Time!**

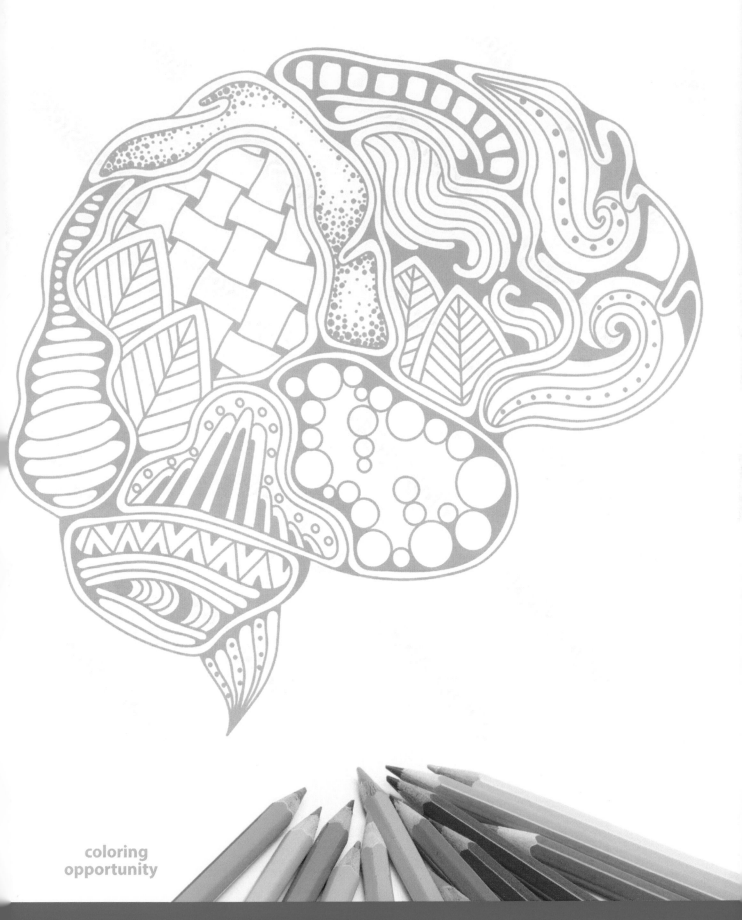

coloring
opportunity

Man, Loops Crew...

When you start succeeding, you never stop.

Well, it looks like we're done here. Thanks for letting us decorate the mini ramp.

Done here?

You aren't close to done.

What do you mean?

Once the cement dries...

Answer Keys

Solomon Island Secrets Crossword

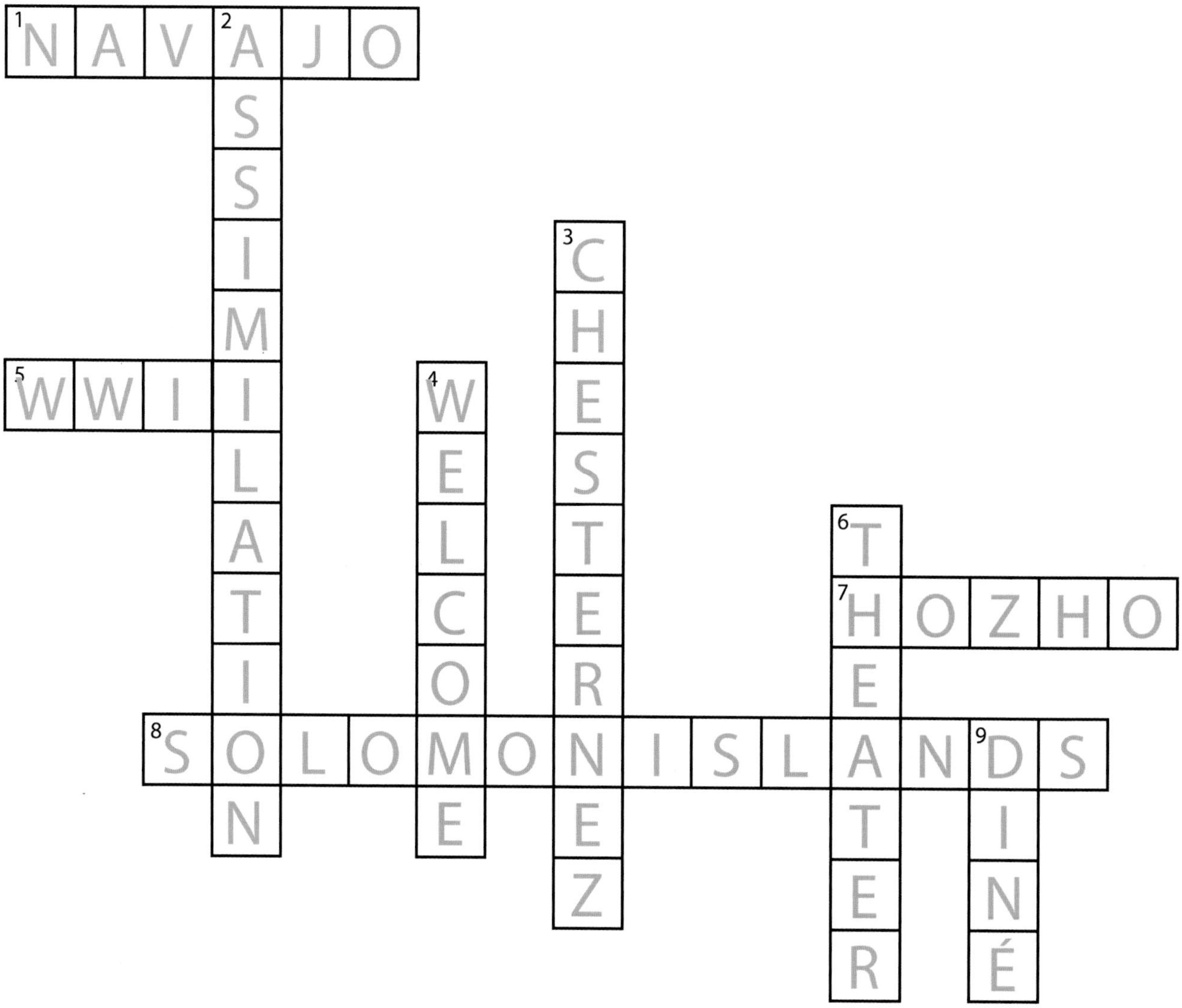
1 NAVAJO
2 ASSIMILATION
3 CHESTERNEZ
4 WELCOME
5 WWII
6 THEATER
7 HOZHO
8 SOLOMONISLANDS
9 DINÉ

Nervous System Word Search

```
O J X O B A R O R E C E P T O R A P
C D G A W M W X T E M P O R A L V A
C D E C E N T R A L R I R Y I G C R
I P H O T O R E C E P T O R U Z E I
P J A W R C N E F R O N T A L C R E
I S Q G N C E R E B E L L U M Y E T
T O L S H E O I V M N G A F H L B A
A P E R I P H E R A L B V E T O R L
L C H E M O R E C E P T O R T B U V
Q T H E R M O R E C E P T O R E M J
I I N T C X B R A I N S T E M F L B
W J P I E N E U R O N Z N A Q I N M
```

Crack the Code Information Review

The Second World War involved over t h i r t y countries in a conflict mainly between the a l l i e s and the a x i s. These two sides fough on two fronts, one in Europe and the other in the P a c i f i c, where the Solomon Islands became a fierce battleground. One the of the essential features of that theater was wartime m e s s a g i n g.

Many N a t i v e Americans enlisted in the military during WWII due to thei loyalty to the l a n d. Using a strategy developed in the first World War, the Marines recruited 29 men from the N a v a j o to create a code using their complex language that had never been w r i t t e n down to help keep messages both secret and easily translated. This code was so effective the Marine recruited more than 3 0 0 Code Talkers by the end of the war.

While the United States appreciated the Navajo in WWII, this was not always the case. In 1864, 1 2 ,0 0 0 Navajo were forced to walk from Arizona to New Mexico, and almost 2 ,0 0 0 died on the journey. Schools were set up to teach Navajo children the " A m e r i c a n W a y " of life to try and eliminate their culture.

The Navajo, or t h e D i n é, survived this and held on to their belief that everyone and everything is connected. Their belief called the H o z h o teaches one "to walk in b e a u t y" and is found deeply entwined in their culture.

A-MAZE-ing Brain

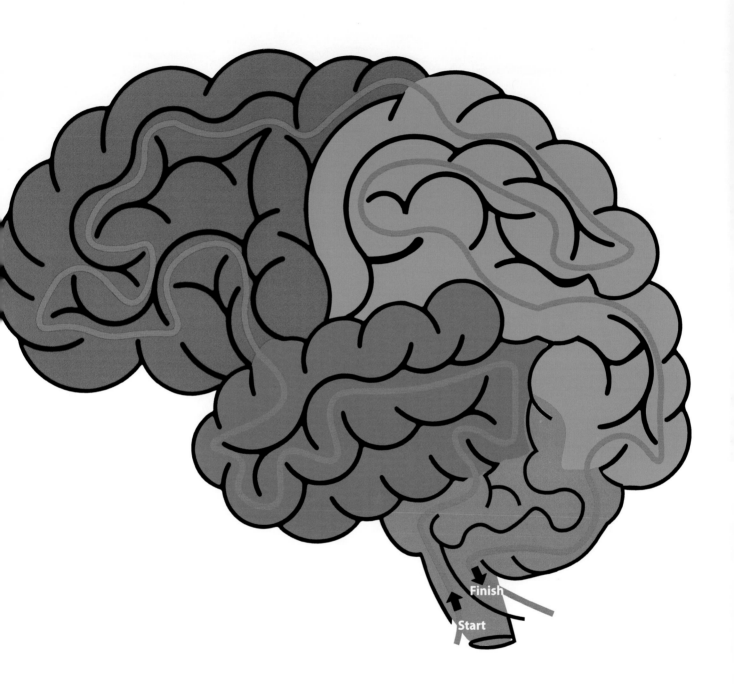

Start

Finish

A-MAZE-ing Brain - Fill in the Blank

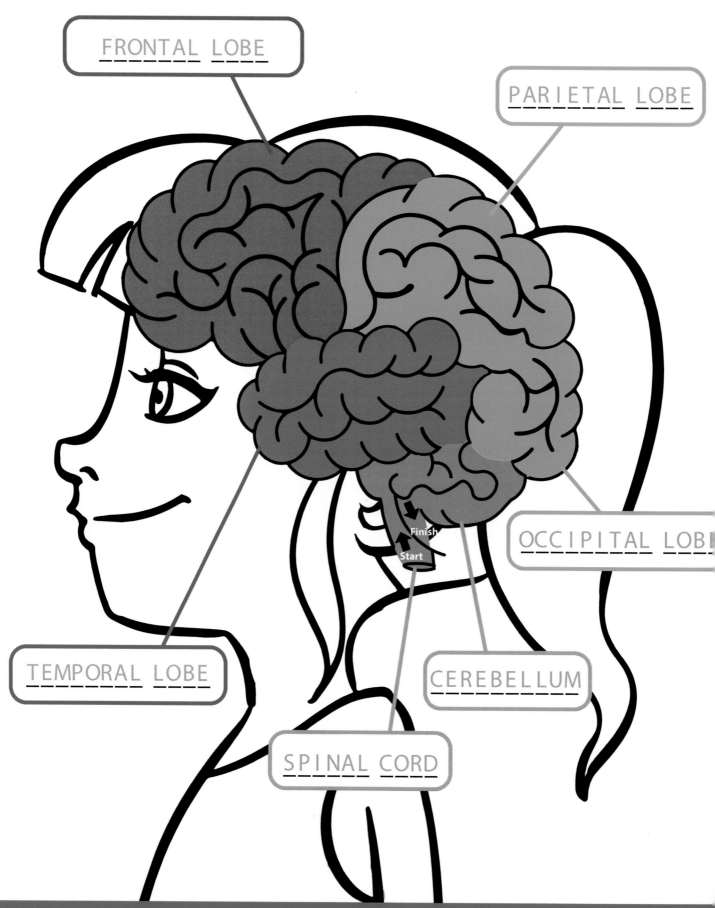

FRONTAL LOBE

PARIETAL LOBE

OCCIPITAL LOBE

TEMPORAL LOBE

CEREBELLUM

SPINAL CORD

Finish

Start

Brain Bop Information Review

The nervous system is <u>Y O U</u> ! The way it works is by sensing what is happening outside your body and sending <u>S I G N A L S</u> to other parts inside your body about how to act in response. Your <u>C E N T R A L</u> nervous system is made up of your brain and spinal cord.

The <u>P E R I P H E R A L</u> nervous system is composed of all the nerves branching from your spinal cord and throughout your body.

In the body, your brain plays the part of <u>C O M M A N D E R</u>, receiving and interpreting information, and then sending out orders to the rest of the body.

The three main parts of the brain are the <u>C E R E B R U M</u>, cerebellum, and brain <u>S T E M</u>. The cerebrum is responsible for thoughts and <u>V O L U N T A R Y</u> motor functions.

The <u>C E R E B E L L U M</u> is the part in charge of balance and posture. The brain stem helps keep you alive by controlling the activities you don't think about - for example, involuntary activities like <u>B R E A T H I N G</u> and swallowing.

Your brain uses millions of nerve cells, called <u>N E U R O N S</u>, that form long chains branching out from your spinal cord and to the rest of your body. These important cells help send messages between the body and <u>B R A I N</u>. The three types of neurons are called <u>S E N S O R Y</u> neurons, <u>M O T O R</u> neurons, and interneurons.

Activity	Nerve(s)
Without moving your head, look at the ceiling.	2
Smile, frown, furrow your brows.	7
Shake your head "no."	11
Stick out your tongue.	12
Look at a sign from far away.	2
Eat a few bites of a snack.	5 9
Cover one eye. Can you see as well with your right eye as your left?	2
Listen to your favorite song. Try to stand on one leg for a count of 10.	8
Jump up and down 10 times, or until your feel your heart beat a bit faster.	10
Take a deep sniff of your favorite smell: cinnamon, mint, pine trees.	1
Look down at your nose.	4
Say a Sentence Outloud.	9 10
Look left and right without turning your head.	3 6

1 Olfactory (ol-fak-tuh-ree) Smell.

2 Optic (op-tik) Vision.

3 Oculomotor (awk-you-low-mo-tor) Moving eyes up, down, toward your center. Moving eyelids.

4 Trochlear (troke-lee-ur) Moving eyes down and in.

5 Trigeminal (tri-gem-ih-null) Sensations of the face. Chewing and biting. Its name means 3x twins—each side of this nerve has three branches!

6 Abducens (ab-doo-senz) Moving eyes away your center. Abduct = to take away.

7 Facial (fay-shull) Taste, expression, and facial and scalp movements.

8 Vestibulolcochlear (ves-ti-byoo-lo-coke-lee-ur) Hearing and balance.

9 Glossopharyngeal (gloss-o-fah-ring ee-uhl) Sensory and motor. Taste, throa swallowing.

10 Vagus (vay-gus) Throat, voice, coughing: glands, digestion, heart rate, respiration.

11 Accessory (ak-cess-uh-ree) Rotating head, shrugging shoulders, raising chin.

12 Hypoglossal (hi-po-gloss-uhl) Moving your tongue.

CREATED WITH LOVE

BY THE

KNOW YOURSELF TEAM

 KnowYourself.com KnowYourselfOAK KnowYourselfOAK